The Fresh Load

Written by
Jill Atkins

Illustrated by
Andy Hamilton

Ransom

Martin is going on a trip in his truck.

The truck has a load of beetroot, carrots and sweetcorn in the back.

Martin will bring them to the shop.
Then the shop will sell them.

Now the truck is in gear.

Go, truck, go!

The truck starts to go along the road.

Then ... up pops a rabbit.

Eek! No!

Martin stops the truck.
He looks at the rabbit.

"Rabbit," he yells. "Stop and look
if you need to cross the road."

Rabbit hops up into the truck.
He can see lots of carrots.

"Yum! I like carrots!"

Go, truck, go!

Martin and his truck set off,
but soon … up darts a rat.

Eek! No!

Martin stops the truck.
He looks at the rat.

"Rat," he yells. "Stop and look
if you need to cross the road."

Rat nips up into the truck.
Now he can smell beetroot.

"Yum! I like beetroot!"

Go, truck, go!

Off they go again, but soon …
a hen flits into the road.

Eek! No!

Martin stops the truck.
He looks at the hen.

"Hen," he yells. "Stop and look
if you need to cross the road."

Hen flaps up into the truck.
She sniffs the air.

"Sweetcorn! Yum! I like sweetcorn!"

"I have had three stops," moans Martin. "I need to get to the shop soon or my beetroots, carrots and sweetcorn will go bad."

At the shop, up pop the rabbit, rat and hen. They creep down the steps of the truck.

"Yum, yum!" they yell as they run off.

Martin looks in the back of the truck.
He gets a big shock.

"No carrots? No beetroot? No sweetcorn?"
he yells.

Martin moans and groans. "Now I will have to go back for a fresh load!"

"But if I see you again, rabbit, rat and hen … I will not stop for you!"